POEMS

Blend Endings
and the magic 'e'

smart phonics

Written by:

Sandra Titchener

Illustrated by:

Clive Taylor

Stella Yang

Jim Storey

SMART KiDS

Blend Endings

ISBN 0-9582370-5-0

Smart Kids Ltd
PO Box 128009
Auckland 1005
New Zealand

Tel (0064) 9 579 9672
Fax (0064) 9 579 9678
www.smartkidscatalog.com

Contents

I Wish...

I wish I had a wooden raft,
To drift upon the sea.
I'd travel to lands far away,
Ruft my dog and me.

I wish I had a magic rug,
All soft with colours bright.
To lift me high above the clouds,
Swiftly out of sight.

I'd go to far off places,
If wishes would come true.
To find another special gift,
Which I'd bring home for you.

Oldy Mouldy Bread

Oldy mouldy brown bread,
Sitting on the bench.
Oldy mouldy brown bread,
What an awful stench!

Oldy mouldy brown bread,
Growing bits of green.
Oldy mouldy brown bread,
The worst I've ever seen.

Oldy mouldy brown bread,
Pinch and hold your nose.
Oldy mouldy brown bread,
Smells just like your toes!

I Love...

I love to dance and sing and play,
I love to chat and talk.
I love to run and skip and jump,
I also love to walk.

I love to eat fish fingers,
And drink cold icy milk.
I love to read and paint and draw,
With paints and crayons and chalk.

Stamp! Stomp! Thump!

At the giant's castle,
I tiptoed up the ramp.
I looked into the window,
A light shone from a lamp.

The room was very messy,
It looked just like a dump.
Suddenly, I heard a **BUMP**,
A **STAMP**, a **STOMP**, a **THUMP!**

I knew it was the giant,
My heart began to jump.
I'd been told this big plump giant,
Could really be a grump!

I decided not to hang around,
I decided I would run.
To be caught and eaten by a giant,
Wouldn't be much fun!

The Magic Land

Above the clouds, way past the wind,
There is a magic land.
Where fairy people sing and dance,
Upon the rainbow sand.

They love to play with all their friends,
And wave around their wands.
They love to sprinkle fairy dust,
Upon the sparkling ponds.

Inky, Winky, Wonky

Inky, winky, wonky,
Grandpa had a donkey.
It couldn't bray,
So cried all day.
Inky, winky, wonky!

Inky, danky, dunky,
Grandma had a monkey.
It drank a drink,
And turned bright pink.
Inky, danky, dunky!

Inkle, winkle, tinkle,
My friend's eyes can twinkle.
He smiles and blinks,
Then gives a wink.
Inkle, winkle, tinkle!

Ants In His Pants

One, two, three, four, five,
The giant counts his toes.
Six, seven, eight, nine, ten,
He chants, "Fee fi, fee, foe!"

One, two, three, four, five,
He saw ten hunting ants.
Six, seven, eight, nine, ten,
The ants went up his pants!

AHHHHH!

The Grunch

Today I met a creature,
He said he was a Grunch.
He shook my hand and asked me,
To sit with him for lunch.

His mouth was full of pointy teeth,
His back was very hunched.
And when he started eating,
He munched and crunched and munched!

Was this Grunch a crazy dream?
Or was this creature true?
I really can't make up my mind,
So I'll leave it up to you!

Th Ghostly P st!

We have a spooky attic,
Full of sticky webs and dust.
The key to open up the door,
Is covered all in rust.

We think a ghost is stirring,
In the rusty old sea chest.
I'm scared, but Mum and Dad they say,
He's just a 'ghostly pest'.

I think he is a sailor,
Who got lost at sea one day.
In a gusty storm or still white mist,
Now it's **here** he wants to stay!

Magic 'e' Rhymes

As I Was Walking Round The Lake

As I was walking round the lake
I met a little rattlesnake,
I gave him so much ice-cream cake
It made his little belly ache.

Anon

Nine Mice From Fice

There once were nine mice from Fice,
Who dined on buckets of rice,
They grew fat and wide,
And wobbled with pride,
For now they would cost twice the price!

Sandra Titchener

An Old Gnome From Rome

There once was an old gnome from Rome,
Who travelled the globe all alone.
He told funny jokes,
Bathed in fizzy Coke,
And juggled great balls of stone!

Sandra Titchener

A Duke Born In June

There once was a duke born in June,
Who never could sing songs in tune.
So he then used his flute,
To hoot and to toot,
Under the huge midnight moon.

Sandra Titchener

The Magic 'e' Song

Have you met the magic e, the magic e, the magic e?
Have you met the magic e, when it casts its spell?

It changes words like **man** to **mane**, **cap** to **cape**, **tap** to **tape**,
It changes words like **mat** to **mate**, it's bossy can't you see?

It changes words like **rip** to **ripe**, **strip** to **stripe**, **grip** to **gripe**,
It changes words like **quit** to **quite**, it's clever can't you see?

Have you met the magic e, the magic e, the magic e?
Have you met the magic e, when it casts its spell?

It changes words like **not** to **note**, **mop** to **mope**, **slop** to **slope**,
It changes words like **rob** to **robe**, it's magic can't you see?

It's sometimes called **policeman e**, the **silent e**, the **magic e**,
It's even called a **split digraph**, it's brilliant can't you see?

Have you met the magic e, the magic e, the magic e?
It's clever, silent and so smart, I'm sure that you'll agree.

 Sing to the tune of 'Have You Seen The Muffin Man?'